W9-ASO-537

THE THIRTEEN DAYS OF YULE

THE THIRTEEN DAYS OF YULE

Introduction by
Anthony Murray

Pictures by Nonny Hogrogian

Thomas Y. Crowell Company
New York

 Printed in Belgium. L.C. Card 68-21606

1 2 3 4 5 6 7 8 9 10

"The Thirteen Days of Yule" is the Scottish version of an old carol that the reader may know as "The Twelve Days of Christmas."

Carols date back to the fifteenth century. And though today we associate them exclusively with Christmas, it was not always thus. Any festive occasion called for caroling.

But a carol was not always sung. It could be a game or a dance. Here's how it was played as a fireside parlor game in the nineteenth century.

The leader started by reciting the first day's gift which in turn was repeated by all the players. Then the leader said the first and second day's gifts together, which were again repeated by the players. Then the first, second, and third days' gifts, and so on, until every gift for all the days had been mentioned by each player in turn. A mistake resulted in a forfeit on the part of the player who erred.

As a dance, which may have been its original form (the word *carol* is derived from Old French meaning a dance in a ring enlivened by song), a king was selected. The dancers circled around him. For each day sung, he chose from the circle of dancers someone to symbolize that day's gift. In the north of France this same game is called *Les dons de l'an.*

English-speaking people have sung it as "The Twelve Days of Christmas." In the west of France it is called *Le foi de la Loi.*

But the Scottish version that follows may well offer more pleasure than others, for it contains one more delicious day of joyous giving, singing, and happy dancing. And its gifts are far more exotic than either the French or the English.

Imagine receiving an Arabian baboon. Or three hinds a merry hunting. Or three goldspinks. Or a gray goose. And most of the gifts in this Scottish version come in threes, which brings us even closer to the pagan times when cumulative verses like this are said to have originated.

ANTHONY MURRAY

The King sent his lady on the first Yule day
A papingo-ay!
Who learns my carol and carries it away?

The King sent his lady on the second Yule day
Three partriks, a papingo—ay!
Who learns my carol and carries it away?

The King sent his lady on the third Yule day
Three plovers, three partriks, a papingo-ay!
Who learns my carol and carries it away?

The King sent his lady on the fourth Yule day
A goose that was gray,
Three plovers, three partriks, a papingo—ay!
Who learns my carol and carries it away?

The King sent his lady on the fifth Yule day
Three starlings, a goose that was gray,
Three plovers, three partriks, a papingo—ay!
Who learns my carol and carries it away?

The King sent his lady on the sixth Yule day
Three goldspinks, three starlings, a goose that was gray,
Three plovers, three partriks, a papingo-ay!
Who learns my carol and carries it away?

The King sent his lady on the seventh Yule day
A bull that was broon,
Three goldspinks, three starlings, a goose that was gray,
Three plovers, three partriks, a papingo—ay!
Who learns my carol and carries it away?

The King sent his lady on the eighth Yule day
Three ducks a merry laying, a bull that was broon,
Three goldspinks, three starlings, a goose that was gray,
Three plovers, three partriks, a papingo-ay!
Who learns my carol and carries it away?

The King sent his lady on the ninth Yule day
Three swans a merry swimming,
Three ducks a merry laying, a bull that was broon,
Three goldspinks, three starlings, a goose that was gray,
Three plovers, three partriks, a papingo-ay!
Who learns my carol and carries it away?

The King sent his lady on the tenth Yule day
An Arabian baboon!
Three swans a merry swimming,
Three ducks a merry laying, a bull that was broon,
Three goldspinks, three starlings, a goose that was gray,
Three plovers, three partriks, a papingo-ay!
Who learns my carol and carries it away?

The King sent his lady on the eleventh Yule day
Three hinds a merry hunting,
An Arabian baboon!
Three swans a merry swimming,
Three ducks a merry laying, a bull that was broon,
Three goldspinks, three starlings, a goose that was gray,
Three plovers, three partriks, a papingo—ay!
Who learns my carol and carries it away?

The King sent his lady on the twelfth Yule day
Three maids a merry dancing, three hinds a merry hunting,
An Arabian baboon!
Three swans a merry swimming,
Three ducks a merry laying, a bull that was broon,
Three goldspinks, three starlings, a goose that was gray,
Three plovers, three partriks, a papingo-ay!
Who learns my carol and carries it away?

The King sent his lady on the thirteenth Yule day
Three stalks o' merry corn,
Three maids a merry dancing, three hinds a merry hunting,
An Arabian baboon!
Three swans a merry swimming,
Three ducks a merry laying, a bull that was broon,
Three goldspinks, three starlings, a goose that was gray,
Three plovers, three partriks, a papingo—ay!
Who learns my carol and carries it away?

Printed in Belgium